ndrew
rodie

Improving Spelling

for ages 10–11

A & C Black • London

INTRODUCTION

Improving Spelling for Ages 10–11 features 42 sets of words, chosen to complement and extend the programme of activities that pupils will have experienced through 'Letters and Sounds'. The pupils will not need to work slavishly through the lists of words. However, if the lists are used on a regular basis as the focus for a short activity, they will help to provide a structured approach to improving pupils' skills in both reading and spelling.

Most pupils enjoy the security of following a repeated pattern in their work. Accordingly, each set of words is presented in two styles of sheet with which the pupils will soon become familiar:

SHEET A

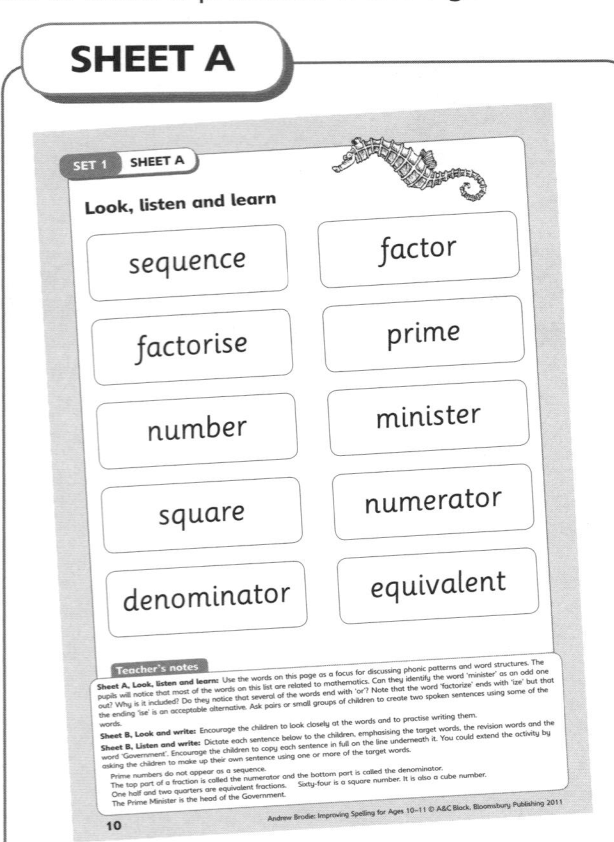

SET 1 SHEET A

Look, listen and learn

sequence	factor
factorise	prime
number	minister
square	numerator
denominator	equivalent

Teacher's notes

Sheet A, Look, listen and learn: Use the words on this page as a focus for discussing phonic patterns and word structures. The pupils will notice that most of the words on this list are related to mathematics. Can they identify the word 'minister' as an odd one out? Why is it included? Do they notice that several of the words end with 'or'? Note that the word 'factorize' ends with 'ize' but that the ending 'ise' is an acceptable alternative. Ask pairs or small groups of children to create two spoken sentences using some of the words.

Sheet B, Look and write: Encourage the children to look closely at the words and to practise writing them.

Sheet B, Listen and write: Dictate each sentence below to the children, emphasising the target words, the revision words and the word 'Government'. Encourage the children to copy each sentence in full on the line underneath it. You could extend the activity by asking the children to make up their own sentence using one or more of the target words.

Prime numbers do not appear as a sequence.
The top part of a fraction is called the numerator and the bottom part is called the denominator.
One half and two quarters are equivalent fractions. Sixty-four is a square number. It is also a cube number.
The Prime Minister is the head of the Government.

10 Andrew Brodie: Improving Spelling for Ages 10–11 © A&C Black, Bloomsbury Publishing 2011

Sheet A features the 10 focus words to encourage the children to:

Look, listen and learn

This sheet can be:

- Displayed on the whiteboard for discussion.
- Copied on to card and cut up to make matching cards.
- Displayed on the wall as 'Words of the Week'.

Encouraging the children to 'sound-talk' the words. For example, the word pick can be sound-talked 'p-i-c-k' but be careful not to add 'uh' to sounds, i.e. say 'p' not 'puh'!

SHEET B

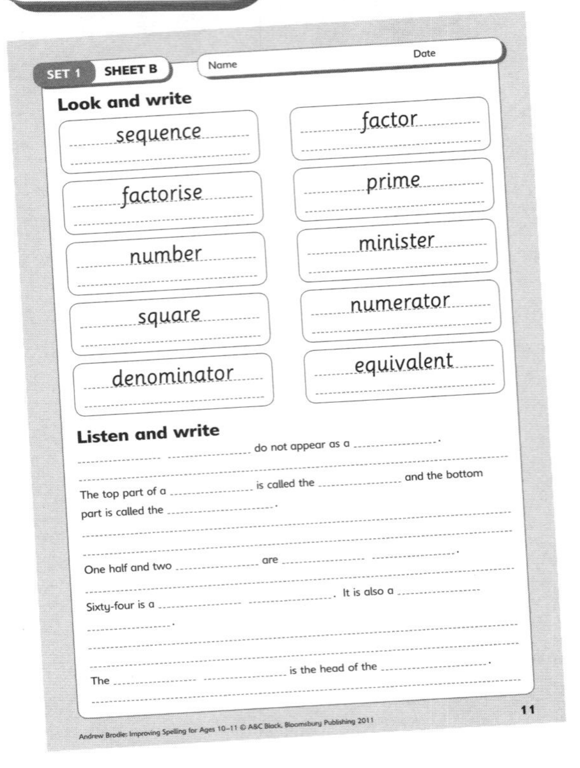

SET 1 SHEET B Name Date

Look and write

sequence	factor
factorise	prime
number	minister
square	numerator
denominator	equivalent

Listen and write

.... do not appear as a ....

The top part of a .... is called the .... and the bottom part is called the ....

One half and two .... are ....

Sixty-four is a .... It is also a ....

The .... is the head of the ....

Andrew Brodie: Improving Spelling for Ages 10–11 © A&C Black, Bloomsbury Publishing 2011 11

Sheet B provides practice activities:

Look and write
Encourages the children to look carefully at the structure of each word.

Listen and write
Encourages the children to listen carefully to the phonemes within each word, to help them to segment the word for spelling.

This sheet can be:

- Displayed on the whiteboard for discussion.
- Photocopied as individual activity sheets.
- Cut in half to make two separate activity sheets.

The book also features five sheets that can be copied and enlarged to make Spelling Strategy Posters, as recommended in 'Letters and Sounds'. You can use these as a focus for discussing strategies that pupils can employ when learning new spellings.

CONTENTS

PUPIL RECORD SHEET

You could record your pupils' progress using the 'traffic light' system: red for not yet secure, orange for secure, green for competent.

Name																														
Set 1																														
Set 2																														
Set 3																														
Set 4																														
Set 5																														
Set 6																														
Set 7																														
Set 8																														
Set 9																														
Set 10																														
Set 11																														
Set 12																														
Set 13																														
Set 14																														
Set 15																														
Set 16																														
Set 17																														
Set 18																														
Set 19																														
Set 20																														
Set 21																														
Set 22																														
Set 23																														
Set 24																														
Set 25																														
Set 26																														
Set 27																														
Set 28																														
Set 29																														
Set 30																														
Set 31																														
Set 32																														
Set 33																														
Set 34																														
Set 35																														
Set 36																														
Set 37																														
Set 38																														
Set 39																														
Set 40																														
Set 41																														
Set 42																														

To help me with spelling
I can use . . .

Syllables

by breaking words into chunks.

Look:

horizontal

To help me with spelling
I can use . . .

Base words

Some words are based
on other words.

Look:

symmetrical

The base word is **symmetry**.

To add the cal ending we need to replace the final y with an i.

To help me with spelling
I can use . . .

Similar words

Some words are similar to other words.

Look:

confidence

independence

Both words have ...dence.

To help me with spelling
I can use . . .

Mnemonics

If I'm really stuck I can make up a phrase or sentence to help me remember.

Look:

beauty

If I am stuck on spelling a word I can . . .

1. use **phonics** to help me.
2. try breaking a big word into **syllables**.
3. think about whether it's made from a **base word**.
4. think about **similar words**.
5. **look** for the word.
6. **ask** for help.
7. use **mnemonics** to learn the word.

Look, listen and learn

sequence	factor
factorize	prime
number	minister
square	numerator
denominator	equivalent

Teacher's notes

Sheet A, Look, listen and learn: Use the words on this page as a focus for discussing phonic patterns and word structures. The pupils will notice that most of the words on this list are related to mathematics. Can they identify the word 'minister' as an odd one out? Why is it included? Do they notice that three of the words end with 'or'? Note that the word 'factorize' ends with 'ize' but that the ending 'ise' is an acceptable alternative. Ask pairs or small groups of children to create two spoken sentences using some of the words.

Sheet B, Look and write: Encourage the children to look closely at the words and to practise writing them.

Sheet B, Listen and write: Dictate each sentence below to the children, emphasising the target words, the revision words and the word 'government'. Encourage the children to copy each sentence in full on the line underneath it. You could extend the activity by asking the children to make up their own sentence using one or more of the target words.

Prime numbers do not appear as a sequence.
The top part of a fraction is called the numerator and the bottom part is called the denominator.
One half and two quarters are equivalent fractions. Sixty-four is a square number. It is also a cube number.
The Prime Minister is the head of the government.

Name Date

Look and write

sequence

factor

factorize

prime

number

minister

square

numerator

denominator

equivalent

Listen and write

________ ________ do not appear as a ________.

The top part of a ________ is called the ________ and the bottom part is called the ________.

One half and two ________ are ________ ________.

Sixty-four is a ________ ________. It is also a ________ ________.

The ________ ________ is the head of the ________.

SET 2 SHEET A

Look, listen and learn

half	quarter
third	fifth
eighth	sixth
ninth	tenth
twelfth	twentieth

Teacher's notes

Sheet A, Look, listen and learn: Use the words on this page as a focus for discussing phonic patterns and word structures. The pupils will notice that all of the words on this list are concerned with number and are all the names for fractions, though many represent 'ordinal' numbers as well, i.e. they represent positions in a series. Ask pairs or small groups of children to create two spoken sentences using some of the words.

Sheet B, Look and write: Encourage the children to look closely at the words and to practise writing them.

Sheet B, Listen and write: Dictate each sentence below to the children, emphasising the target words and the word 'mathematics'. Encourage the children to copy each sentence in full on the line underneath it. You could extend the activity by asking the children to make up their own sentence using one or more of the target words.

My brother had half of the cake but my sister and I only had a quarter each.
The fraction one fifth is bigger than the fraction one sixth. One twentieth is quite a small fraction.
Three ninths is equivalent to one third. Three tenths is equivalent to six twentieths.

Name Date

Look and write

half	quarter
third	fifth
eighth	sixth
ninth	tenth
twelfth	twentieth

Listen and write

My brother had ________________ of the cake but my sister and I only had a ________________ each.

The ________________ one ________________ is bigger than the ________________ one ________________.

One ____________________ is quite a small ____________________.

Three ________________ is equivalent to one ________________.

Three ________________ is equivalent to six ________________.

SET 3 SHEET A

Look, listen and learn

hundredth	thousandth
decimal	percentage
per cent	fraction
thousand	million
billion	approximate

Teacher's notes

Sheet A, Look, listen and learn: Use the words on this page as a focus for discussing phonic patterns and word structures. The pupils will notice that all of the words on this list are concerned with number and that some of the words are closely related. Ask pairs or small groups of children to create two spoken sentences using some of the words.

Sheet B, Look and write: Encourage the children to look closely at the words and to practise writing them.

Sheet B, Listen and write: Dictate each sentence below to the children, emphasising the target words and the revision words. Encourage the children to copy each sentence in full on the line underneath it. You could extend the activity by asking the children to make up their own sentence using one or more of the target words.

One centimetre is one hundredth of a metre. One millilitre is one thousandth of a litre.
The decimal zero point five is equivalent to the fraction one half.
The percentage ninety per cent is equivalent to the fraction nine tenths. A thousand millions make one billion.

Name Date

Look and write

hundredth	thousandth
decimal	percentage
per cent	fraction
thousand	million
billion	approximate

Listen and write

One __________ is one __________ of a metre.

One __________ is one __________ of a litre.

The __________ zero point five is equivalent to the __________ one half.

The __________ ninety ______ ______ is equivalent to the __________ nine __________.

A __________ __________ make one __________.

Look, listen and learn

approximately	estimate
roughly	integer
positive	negative
multiple	remainder
quotient	divisible

Teacher's notes

Sheet A, Look, listen and learn: Use the words on this page as a focus for discussing phonic patterns and word structures. The pupils will notice that all of the words on this list are concerned with mathematics. Some of the words are apparently difficult to spell but by splitting them into their syllables or, even further, segmenting them into their phonemes they can become much easier. Note that the word 'integer' features a 'soft g', ie the phoneme /j/. Discuss the phoneme /sh/ represented by the grapheme 'ti' in the word 'quotient'. Ask pairs or small groups of children to create two spoken sentences using some of the words.

Sheet B, Look and write: Encourage the children to look closely at the words and to practise writing them.

Sheet B, Listen and write: Dictate each sentence below to the children, emphasising the target words and the revision words. Encourage the children to copy each sentence in full on the line underneath it. You could extend the activity by asking the children to make up their own sentence using one or more of the target words.

The height of my room is approximately two and a half metres.
It's a good idea to make an estimate before working out the answer.
Positive integers are whole numbers above zero. Negative integers are whole numbers below zero.
When one number is exactly divisible by another number there is no remainder.

Name Date

Look and write

approximately	estimate
roughly	integer
positive	negative
multiple	remainder
quotient	divisible

Listen and write

The ______ of my room is __________ two and a ______ metres.

It's a good idea to make an ________ before working out the ________.

________ ________ are whole numbers above ________.

________ ________ are whole numbers below ________.

When one number is exactly ________ by another number there is no ________.

SET 5 SHEET A

Look, listen and learn

calculator	display
recurring	occurring
memory	operation
occurred	occurrence
memories	memorize

Teacher's notes

Sheet A, Look, listen and learn: Use the words on this page as a focus for discussing phonic patterns and word structures. Again many of these words are used in relation to mathematics, though obviously all of them can be used in other contexts. Note the spelling of 'memorize' – spelt this way, with the z, is the standard spelling shown in the Oxford dictionary but many people use the spelling 'memorise', which is also correct. Breaking the words into their syllables and discussing features of each syllable in relation to their letters and sounds can make them easier to spell and remember. Ask pairs or small groups of children to create two spoken sentences using some of the words.

Sheet B, Look and write: Encourage the children to look closely at the words and to practise writing them.

Sheet B, Listen and write: Dictate each sentence below to the children, emphasising the target words and the other focus words. Note that the children will have to use the apostrophe for possession when writing the word 'computer's'. Encourage the children to copy each sentence in full on the line underneath it. You could extend the activity by asking the children to make up their own sentence using one or more of the target words.

The display on my calculator showed three as a recurring digit. Mistakes keep occurring when I press the wrong keys.
My computer's memory is much better than my own! I have good memories from when I was in the reception class.
At first, I found it hard to memorize my multiplication tables.

Name Date

Look and write

calculator	display
recurring	occurring
memory	operation
occurred	occurrence
memories	memorize

Listen and write

The ________ on my ________ showed three as a ________ digit.

________ keep ________ when I press the wrong keys.

My ________ ________ is much better than my own!

I have good ________ from when I was in the ________ class.

At first, I found it hard to ________ my ________ tables.

Look, listen and learn

calculation	method
strategy	operation
symbol	cymbals
equation	equals
equality	puzzle

Teacher's notes

Sheet A, Look, listen and learn: Use the words on this page as a focus for discussing phonic patterns and word structures. Again, most of these words are used in relation to mathematics but note the inclusion of the homophone cymbals. Breaking the words into their syllables and discussing features of each syllable in relation to their letters and sounds can make them easier to spell and remember. Ask pairs or small groups of children to create two spoken sentences using some of the words.

Sheet B, Look and write: Encourage the children to look closely at the words and to practise writing them.

Sheet B, Listen and write: Dictate each sentence below to the children, emphasising the target words and the revision words. Encourage the children to copy each sentence in full on the line underneath it. You could extend the activity by asking the children to make up their own sentence using one or more of the target words.

You can use different calculation methods for a multiplication question but each one should give the same result.
When solving a problem you need to decide which mathematical operation to use.
There is usually a particular strategy for solving each type of puzzle.
You should always look carefully at the symbols in maths questions. Both sides of a mathematical equation should be balanced.

Name Date

Look and write

calculation	method
strategy	operation
symbol	cymbals
equation	equals
equality	puzzle

Listen and write

You can use different ________ ________ for a ________ question but each one should give the same result.

When solving a ________ you need to decide which ________ ________ to use.

There is usually a particular ________ for solving each type of ________.

You should always look carefully at the ________ in maths ________.

Both sides of a ________ ________ should be balanced.

Look, listen and learn

money	bought
expensive	spent
amount	value
valuation	discount
currency	dollar

Teacher's notes

Sheet A, Look, listen and learn: Use the words on this page as a focus for discussing phonic patterns and word structures. What do all the words have in common? Can the pupils name any other currencies? Ask pairs or small groups of children to create two spoken sentences using some of the words.

Sheet B, Look and write: Encourage the children to look closely at the words and to practise writing them.

Sheet B, Listen and write: Dictate each sentence below to the children, emphasising the target words and the revision words. Encourage the children to copy each sentence in full on the line underneath it. You could extend the activity by asking the children to make up their own sentence using one or more of the target words.

I didn't have enough money for the new camera because it was too expensive.
I found another camera at a discount price so I bought that one instead.
The dollar is the unit of currency in the United States of America.
What is the current value of the pound against the dollar?
I spent too much money so I only have a small amount left.

Name Date

Look and write

money

bought

expensive

spent

amount

value

valuation

discount

currency

dollar

Listen and write

I didn't have enough ________________ for the new camera because it was too ________________.

I found another camera at a ________________ price so I ________________ that one ________________.

The ________________ is the unit of ________________ in the United States of America.

What is the ________________ ________________ of the ________________ against the ________________?

I ________________ too much ________________ so I only have a small ________________ left.

Look, listen and learn

graph	pictogram
frequency	axis
axes	diagram
mean	median
mode	range

Teacher's notes

Sheet A, Look, listen and learn: Use the words on this page as a focus for discussing phonic patterns and word structures. Ensure that the children understand the meaning of each word and can pronounce each one. Note the word 'axes', pronounced /a/ /k/ /s/ /ee/ /z/. Ask pairs or small groups of children to create two spoken sentences using some of the words – can they make up some sentences that are related to maths but others that are related to non-mathematical ideas?

Sheet B, Look and write: Encourage the children to look closely at the words and to practise writing them.

Sheet B, Listen and write: Dictate each sentence below to the children, emphasising the target words and the revision words. Encourage the children to copy each sentence in full on the line underneath it. You could extend the activity by asking the children to make up their own sentence using one or more of the target words.

A graph has two axes, a horizontal axis and a vertical axis. It is usually easy to interpret data on a pictogram.
The frequency of different pieces of data can be shown on various types of graph.
The range of the data is the difference between the highest value and the lowest value.
The median is the middle value when a set of values are arranged in order of size.

Name Date

Look and write

graph	pictogram
frequency	axis
axes	diagram
mean	median
mode	range

Listen and write

A ________ has two ________, a horizontal ________ and a vertical ________.

____

It is usually easy to ________ data on a ________.

____

The ________ of different pieces of data can be shown on ________ types of ________.

____

The ________ of the data is the ________ between the highest ________ and the lowest ________.

____

____

The ________ is the middle value when a set of ________ are ________ in order of size.

____

Look, listen and learn

maximum	minimum
popular	certain
uncertain	probable
possible	impossible
likely	likelihood

Teacher's notes

Sheet A, Look, listen and learn: Use the words on this page as a focus for discussing phonic patterns and word structures. Again, many of these words are used in relation to mathematics, though obviously all of them can be used in other contexts. Discuss the word 'probability', which is not on the list, and compare it to the words 'probable' and 'possibility'. Ask pairs or small groups of children to create two spoken sentences using some of the words.

Sheet B, Look and write: Encourage the children to look closely at the words and to practise writing them.

Sheet B, Listen and write: Dictate each sentence below to the children, emphasising the target words and revision words. Encourage the children to copy each sentence in full on the line underneath it. You could extend the activity by asking the children to make up their own sentence using one or more of the target words..

The maximum number of people who can fit on the bus is forty-six. A minimum of four people should carry the netball posts.
It is possible to get snow in July but it is very unlikely. What is the likelihood of getting snow in November?
I am not certain which is the most popular colour of car.

Name Date

Look and write

maximum	minimum
popular	certain
uncertain	probable
possible	impossible
likely	likelihood

Listen and write

The ____________ number of ____________ who can fit on the bus is ____________.

A ____________ of four ____________ should carry the netball posts.

It is ____________ to get snow in July but it is very ____________.

What is the ____________ of getting snow in ____________?

I am not ____________ which is the most ____________ colour of car.

Look, listen and learn

measure	measurement
compare	comparison
length	width
height	depth
narrow	shallow

Teacher's notes

Sheet A, Look, listen and learn: Use the words on this page as a focus for discussing phonic patterns and word structures. All of the words are related to measurement. Ask pairs or small groups of children to create two spoken sentences using some of the words.

Sheet B, Look and write: Encourage the children to look closely at the words and to practise writing them.

Sheet B, Listen and write: Dictate each sentence below to the children, emphasising the target words and the revision words. Encourage the children to copy each sentence in full on the line underneath it. You could extend the activity by asking the children to make up their own sentence using one or more of the target words.

We had to compare the measurements of some earthworms.
It was easy to measure the length of each worm then to make comparisons between them.
What is the width of the pool at the shallow end? Is the pool narrower at the shallow end than at the deep end?
What is the depth of the water in the River Thames at Tower Bridge?

Name Date

Look and write

measure

measurement

compare

comparison

length

width

height

depth

narrow

shallow

Listen and write

We had to ____________ the ____________ of some earthworms.

It was easy to ____________ the ____________ of each worm then to make ____________ between them.

What is the ____________ of the pool at the ____________ end?

Is the pool ____________ at the ____________ end than at the deep end?

What is the ____________ of the water in the River ____________ at Tower Bridge?

Look, listen and learn

distance	perimeter
circumference	millimetre
centimetre	metre
kilometre	inches
compasses	protractor

Teacher's notes

Sheet A, Look, listen and learn: Use the words on this page as a focus for discussing phonic patterns and word structures. All of the words are related to measurement. Pupils could compare the ending of 'perimeter' to that of 'metre', 'millimetre', 'centimetre' an 'kilometre'. Point out that, here, the prefix 'milli' represents one-thousandth, 'centi' represents one-hundredth and 'kilo' represents on thousand. Ask pairs or small groups of children to create two spoken sentences using some of the words.

Sheet B, Look and write: Encourage the children to look closely at the words and to practise writing them.

Sheet B, Listen and write: Dictate each sentence below to the children, emphasising the target words. Encourage the children to copy each sentence in full on the line underneath it. You could extend the activity by asking the children to make up their own sentence using one or more of the target words.

The distance measured all round a shape is called its perimeter. The perimeter of a circle is called its circumference.
There are one thousand millimetres in a metre. Circles can be drawn using a pair of compasses.
We measure angles using a protractor.

Name Date

Look and write

distance	perimeter
circumference	millimetre
centimetre	metre
kilometre	inches
compasses	protractor

Listen and write

The ____________ ____________ all round a shape is called its ____________.

The ____________ of a ____________ is called its ____________.

There are one ____________ ____________ in a ____________.

____________ can be drawn using a pair of ____________.

We ____________ ____________ using a ____________.

Look, listen and learn

litre	millilitre
centilitre	cylinder
capacity	volume
area	surface
kilogram	tonne

Teacher's notes

Sheet A, Look, listen and learn: Use the words on this page as a focus for discussing phonic patterns and word structures. All of the words are related to measurement. Ask pairs or small groups of children to create two spoken sentences using some of the words.

Sheet B, Look and write: Encourage the children to look closely at the words and to practise writing them.

Sheet B, Listen and write: Dictate each sentence below to the children, emphasising the target words and the revision words. Encourage the children to copy each sentence in full on the line underneath it. You could extend the activity by asking the children to make up their own sentence using one or more of the target words.

There are one thousand millilitres in a litre. There are one hundred centilitres in a litre.
Liquid can be measured in a measuring cylinder. The reservoir has the capacity to hold a huge volume of water.
There are one thousand kilograms in a tonne.

Name Date

Look and write

litre	millilitre
centilitre	cylinder
capacity	volume
area	surface
kilogram	tonne

Listen and write

There are one ________ ________ in a ________.

____

There are one ________ ________ in a ________.

____

________ can be measured in a measuring ________.

____

The reservoir has the ________ to hold a huge ________ of water.

____

There are one ________ ________ in a ________.

____

SET 13 SHEET A

Look, listen and learn

circumference	concentric
arc	circular
centre	radius
diameter	semi-circle
hemisphere	spherical

Teacher's notes

Sheet A, Look, listen and learn: Use the words on this page as a focus for discussing phonic patterns and word structures. All of the words are related to two dimensional or three dimensional shapes. Ensure that the children understand each word, perhaps by drawing diagrams or by showing them the solid shapes. Note that the prefix 'semi' is derived from the Latin for half, whereas 'hemi' is derived from the Greek for half. Ask pairs or small groups of children to create two spoken sentences using some of the words.

Sheet B, Look and write: Encourage the children to look closely at the words and to practise writing them.

Sheet B, Listen and write: Dictate each sentence below to the children, emphasising the target words and the revision words. Encourage the children to copy each sentence in full on the line underneath it. You could extend the activity by asking the children to make up their own sentence using one or more of the target words.

We live in the northern hemisphere. Different circles with the same centre are concentric.
Draw a circle with a radius of four centimetres. Draw a circle with a diameter of six centimetres.
The planets are spherical in shape.

Name Date

Look and write

circumference	concentric
arc	circular
centre	radius
diameter	semi-circle
hemisphere	spherical

Listen and write

We live in the northern ____________________.

____

Different ________________ with the same ________________ are ________________.

____

Draw a ________________ with a ________________ of four ________________.

____

Draw a ________________ with a ________________ of six ________________.

____

The planets are ________________ in shape.

____

Look, listen and learn

pyramid	prism
tetrahedron	equilateral
isosceles	scalene
rhombus	pentagon
hexagon	cuboid

Teacher's notes

Sheet A, Look, listen and learn: Use the words on this page as a focus for discussing phonic patterns and word structures. Can the pupils identify which words are associated with 2D and which are associated with 3D shapes? Note the use of the prefix 'tetra', derived from the Greek for four. Ask pairs or small groups of children to create two spoken sentences using some of the words.

Sheet B, Look and write: Encourage the children to look closely at the words and to practise writing them.

Sheet B, Listen and write: Dictate each sentence below to the children, emphasising the target words and the revision words. Encourage the children to copy each sentence in full on the line underneath it. You could extend the activity by asking the children to make up their own sentence using one or more of the target words..

A tetrahedron is a pyramid with four triangular faces, including the base.
The pyramids in Egypt each have four triangular faces but they also have a square base.
An equilateral triangle has three equal sides and an isosceles triangle has two equal sides and one of different length.
A scalene triangle has no equal sides. A rhombus has four equal sides but no right angles.

Name Date

Look and write

pyramid	prism
tetrahedron	equilateral
isosceles	scalene
rhombus	pentagon
hexagon	cuboid

Listen and write

A ____________ is a ____________ with four ____________ faces, including the base.

The ____________ in Egypt each have four ____________ faces but they also have a ____________ base.

An ____________ triangle has three equal sides and an ____________ triangle has two equal sides and one of different length.

A ____________ triangle has no equal sides.

A ____________ has four equal sides but no right ____________.

Look, listen and learn

rectangular	pentagonal
hexagonal	heptagon
octagon	octagonal
octopus	quadrilateral
parallelogram	trapezium

Teacher's notes

Sheet A, Look, listen and learn: Use the words on this page as a focus for discussing phonic patterns and word structures. Note the use of the suffix 'al' added to three of the words, but also the alteration of the word 'rectangle' to become 'rectangular'. Can the children think of another word that ends with 'ular'? Ask pairs or small groups of children to create two spoken sentences using some of the words.

Sheet B, Look and write: Encourage the children to look closely at the words and to practise writing them.

Sheet B, Listen and write: Dictate each sentence below to the children, emphasising the target words. Encourage the children to copy each sentence in full on the line underneath it. You could extend the activity by asking the children to make up their own sentence using one or more of the target words.

The main playground is rectangular in shape. The Pentagon is an important building in America, built in a pentagonal shape.
Two British coins are based on the shape of a heptagon. An octopus has eight arms.
A parallelogram and a trapezium are both quadrilaterals.

Name Date

Look and write

rectangular	pentagonal
hexagonal	heptagon
octagon	octagonal
octopus	quadrilateral
parallelogram	trapezium

Listen and write

The main ________ is ________ in shape.

____

The ________ is an ________ building in America, built in a ________ shape.

____

____

Two ________ coins are based on the shape of a ________.

____

An ________ has eight arms.

____

A ________ and a ________ are both ________.

____

____

Look, listen and learn

symmetry	symmetrical
reflection	reflective
mirror	opposite
horizontal	vertical
diagonal	parallel

Teacher's notes

Sheet A, Look, listen and learn: Use the words on this page as a focus for discussing phonic patterns and word structures. The list features mathematical vocabulary, which provides good opportunities for syllabification and segmentation. Ask pairs or small groups of children to create two spoken sentences using some of the words.

Sheet B, Look and write: Encourage the children to look closely at the words and to practise writing them.

Sheet B, Listen and write: Dictate each sentence below to the children, emphasising the target words. Encourage the children to copy each sentence in full on the line underneath it. You could extend the activity by asking the children to make up their own sentence using one or more of the target words.

Some capital letters are symmetrical. We can use a mirror to check for symmetry.
Shiny surfaces are usually very reflective. A graph has a horizontal axis and a vertical axis.
The opposite sides of a rectangle are parallel.

Name Date

Look and write

symmetry	symmetrical
reflection	reflective
mirror	opposite
horizontal	vertical
diagonal	parallel

Listen and write

Some ____________ letters are ____________.

We can use a ____________ to check for ____________.

Shiny ____________ are usually very ____________.

A graph has a ____________ ____________ and a ____________ ____________.

The opposite sides of a ____________ are ____________.

Look, listen and learn

prefix	suffix
biography	autobiography
proverb	preposition
mnemonic	vocabulary
derived	derivation

Teacher's notes

Sheet A, Look, listen and learn: Use the words on this page as a focus for discussing phonic patterns and word structures. The children will notice that all of these words are connected with literacy. Ask pairs or small groups of children to create two spoken sentences using some of the words.

Sheet B, Look and write: Encourage the children to look closely at the words and to practise writing them.

Sheet B, Listen and write: Dictate each sentence below to the children, emphasising the target words. Encourage the children to copy each sentence in full on the line underneath it. You could extend the activity by asking the children to make up their own sentence using one or more of the target words.

The prefix 'bio' is derived from the Greek word bios meaning the course of human life. Do you know much French vocabulary?
You could write your own autobiography or you could write the biography of someone else.
'A rolling stone gathers no moss' is an old proverb. We can use mnemonics to help us remember the spellings of difficult words.

Name Date

Look and write

prefix	suffix
biography	autobiography
proverb	preposition
mnemonic	vocabulary
derived	derivation

Listen and write

The ____________ 'bio' is ____________ from the Greek word bios meaning the course of human life.

Do you know much French ____________?

You could write your own ____________ or you could write the ____________ of someone else.

'A rolling stone gathers no moss' is an old ____________.

We can use ____________ to help us ____________ the spellings of difficult words.

Look, listen and learn

biology	biological
biologist	zoology
zoologist	ecology
ecologist	psychology
psychologist	geology

Teacher's notes

Sheet A, Look, listen and learn: Use the words on this page as a focus for discussing phonic patterns and word structures. The pupils will notice that most of the words end with 'ology' and the remaining words are based on these words. Note the 'silent' or 'unsounded' letter 'p' in 'psychology' and 'psychologist'. Ask pairs or small groups of children to create two spoken sentences using some of the words.

Sheet B, Look and write: Encourage the children to look closely at the words and to practise writing them.

Sheet B, Listen and write: Dictate each sentence below to the children, emphasising the target words. You may wish to look closely at the word organisms before starting the dictation. Encourage the children to copy each sentence in full on the line underneat it. You could extend the activity by asking the children to make up their own sentence using one or more of the target words.

A biologist is an expert in the subject of biology. A zoologist studies science in relation to animals.
A psychologist is an expert of the human mind. Ecology is a branch of biology concerned with organisms and their environmen
Geology is the science of the earth, including the rocks from which it is formed.

Name Date

Look and write

biology

biological

biologist

zoology

zoologist

ecology

ecologist

psychology

psychologist

geology

Listen and write

A ____________ is an ____________ in the subject of ____________.

A ____________ studies ____________ in relation to animals.

A ____________ is an ____________ of the human mind.

____________ is a branch of ____________ concerned with ____________ and their ____________.

____________ is the ____________ of the earth, including the rocks from which it is formed.

Look, listen and learn

electric	electricity
electrical	circuit
diagram	battery
series	parallel
wiring	switch

Teacher's notes

Sheet A, Look, listen and learn: Use the words on this page as a focus for discussing phonic patterns and word structures. All of these words are related to the pupils' work in science and all can give excellent practice of the processes of syllabification and segmentation. Ask pairs or small groups of children to create two spoken sentences using some of the words.

Sheet B, Look and write: Encourage the children to look closely at the words and to practise writing them.

Sheet B, Listen and write: Dictate the passage below to the children, emphasising the target words. Allow the children time to fill in the missing words. You could extend the activity by asking the children to make up their own sentence using one or more of the target words.

To make a bulb light up you need to create a complete electrical circuit. The bulb can be held in a bulb holder, then the end of one wire is connected to one of the terminals on the holder. The other end of the wire is connected to one terminal of the battery. In a similar way, another wire is used to connect the other terminals of the holder and the battery. Now the electricity can flow through the circuit and the bulb will light up. If you wish to switch the light on and off, you can include a switch in your circuit.

Name Date

Look and write

electric	electricity
electrical	circuit
diagram	battery
series	parallel
wiring	switch

Listen and write

To make a bulb light up you need to create a complete ____________________ ____________________. The bulb can be held in a bulb holder, then the end of one wire is ____________________ to one of the ____________________ on the holder. The other end of the wire is ____________________ to one ____________________ of the ____________________.

In a similar way, another wire is used to connect the other ____________________ of the holder and the ____________________. Now the ____________________ can flow through the ____________________ and the bulb will light up. If you wish to ____________________ the light on and off, you can include a ____________________ in your ____________________.

SET 20 SHEET A

Look, listen and learn

observation	accurate
measurements	conclusions
organisms	micro-organisms
dissolving	evaporating
evaporation	habitat

Teacher's notes

Sheet A, Look, listen and learn: Use the words on this page as a focus for discussing phonic patterns and word structures. All of these words are related to the pupils' work in science and all can give excellent practice of the processes of syllabification and segmentation. Ask pairs or small groups of children to create two spoken sentences using some of the words.

Sheet B, Look and write: Encourage the children to look closely at the words and to practise writing them.

Sheet B, Listen and write: Dictate each sentence below to the children, emphasising the target words. Encourage the children to copy each sentence in full on the line underneath it. You could extend the activity by asking the children to make up their own sentence using one or more of the target words.

When studying science we need to make careful observations. Science work usually requires accurate measurements. The observations and measurements help us to reach scientific conclusions. We need to protect the habitats of organisms. Bacteria are micro-organisms.

SET 20 SHEET B

Name Date

Look and write

observation

accurate

measurements

conclusions

organisms

micro-organisms

dissolving

evaporating

evaporation

habitat

Listen and write

When studying ____________ we need to make careful ____________.

____________ work usually requires ____________ ____________.

The ____________ and ____________ help us to reach ____________ ____________.

We need to protect the ____________ of ____________.

Bacteria are ____________.

Look, listen and learn

forces	gravity
friction	magnetism
magnetic	newtons
experiment	mechanism
technology	technological

Teacher's notes

Sheet A, Look, listen and learn: Use the words on this page as a focus for discussing phonic patterns and word structures. All o these words are related to the pupils' work in science and all can give excellent practice of the processes of syllabification and segmentation. Ask pairs or small groups of children to create two spoken sentences using some of the words.

Sheet B, Look and write: Encourage the children to look closely at the words and to practise writing them.

Sheet B, Listen and write: Dictate each sentence below to the children, emphasising the target words and the revision words. Discuss the spelling of the word mathematician before starting the dictation. Ensure that they use a capital letter for the name 'Newton' but point out that the capital is not needed for the unit of measurement of forces, even though this unit is named after hi Encourage the children to copy each sentence in full on the line underneath it. You could extend the activity by asking the children make up their own sentence using one or more of the target words.

Just by dropping a ball we can carry out experiments with the force of gravity. Forces can be measured in newtons.
Sir Isaac Newton was a great mathematician and scientist. A machine may contain more than one mechanism.
Magnetism is an important aspect of technology.

Name Date

Look and write

forces

gravity

friction

magnetism

magnetic

newtons

experiment

mechanism

technology

technological

Listen and write

Just by dropping a ball we can carry out ______ with the ______ of ______.

______ can be measured in ______.

Sir Isaac ______ was a great ______ and ______.

A ______ may contain more than one ______.

______ is an important aspect of ______.

Look, listen and learn

quintuplet	pentathlon
nonagon	quadruplet
triple	triplet
decathlon	decagon
century	centipede

Teacher's notes

Sheet A, Look, listen and learn: Use the words on this page as a focus for discussing phonic patterns and word structures. Do the pupils recognize that all of the words concern numbers? Can they think of other examples of words that contain the prefixes 'quin', 'pent', 'quad', 'tri', 'dec' or 'cent'? They may be interested to know that December was the tenth month of the Roman calend[illegible] Ask pairs or small groups of children to create two spoken sentences using some of the words.

Sheet B, Look and write: Encourage the children to look closely at the words and to practise writing them.

Sheet B, Listen and write: Dictate each sentence below to the children, emphasising the target words and the revision words. Encourage the children to copy each sentence in full on the line underneath it. You could extend the activity by asking the children t[illegible] make up their own sentence using one or more of the target words.

The quintuplets were very famous from the day they were born. Triplets are quite rare but quadruplets are extremely rare. There are five different events in the modern pentathlon. The decathlon is an Olympic event, consisting of ten different events. A centipede has many legs.

Name Date

Look and write

quintuplet	pentathlon
nonagon	quadruplet
triple	triplet
decathlon	decagon
century	centipede

Listen and write

The ____________ were very ____________ from the day they were born.

____________ are quite rare but ____________ are ____________ rare.

There are five different events in the modern ____________.

The ____________ is an Olympic event, ____________ of ten different events.

A ____________ has many legs.

Look, listen and learn

yacht	antique
queue	quay
guard	guardian
grotesque	February
library	medicine

Teacher's notes

Sheet A, Look, listen and learn: Use the words on this page as a focus for discussing phonic patterns and word structures. This list consists of words that have a particularly unusual feature. Using these words as a starting point, you could create a class list of 'freaky' words! Ask pairs or small groups of children to create two spoken sentences using some of the words.

Sheet B, Look and write: Encourage the children to look closely at the words and to practise writing them.

Sheet B, Listen and write: Dictate each sentence below to the children, emphasising the target words. Do the pupils remember to use a capital letter for the name of the 'Guardian'? Encourage the children to copy each sentence in full on the line underneath it. You could extend the activity by asking the children to make up their own sentence using one or more of the target words.

The yacht was tied up at the quay.
The Guardian is a daily newspaper.
There was a queue of people outside the library.
The guard stood very still and looked straight ahead.
I bought an antique cup when I went to London in February.

Name Date

Look and write

yacht	antique
queue	quay
guard	guardian
grotesque	February
library	medicine

Listen and write

The ____________ was tied up at the ____________.

The ____________ stood very still and looked ____________ ahead.

The ____________ is a ____________ newspaper.

I bought an ____________ cup when I went to London in ____________.

There was a ____________ of people outside the ____________.

SET 24 SHEET A

Look, listen and learn

Worcester	Gloucester
Middlesborough	Birmingham
Leominster	Warwick
Berwick-upon-Tweed	Norwich
Carlisle	Folkestone

Teacher's notes

Sheet A, Look, listen and learn: Use the words on this page as a focus for discussing phonic patterns and word structures. What do the pupils notice about the set of words? Do they know that all of these towns are in England? Each name has at least one graphical feature that does not follow conventional phonic rules. Can the pupils think of any towns in your area which have unusual spellings? Ask pairs or small groups of children to create two spoken sentences using some of the words.

Sheet B, Look and write: Encourage the children to look closely at the words and to practise writing them.

Sheet B, Listen and write: Dictate each sentence below to the children, emphasising the target words. You may like to compare the spellings of border and board. Encourage the children to copy each sentence in full on the line underneath it. You could extend the activity by asking the children to make up their own sentence using one or more of the target words.

Dr Foster went to Gloucester! Birmingham is a big city in the central part of England.
Berwick-upon-Tweed is close to the border of Scotland. Warwick has a large castle, which is open to visitors.
In Folkestone you can board the ferry to France.

Name Date

Look and write

Worcester	Gloucester
Middlesborough	Birmingham
Leominster	Warwick
Berwick-upon-Tweed	Norwich
Carlisle	Folkestone

Listen and write

Dr Foster went to ______________ !

______________ is a big city in the ______________ part of England.

______________ is close to the ______________ of Scotland.

______________ has a large ______________, which is open to ______________.

In ______________ you can ______________ the ferry to France.

Look, listen and learn

Edinburgh	Lerwick
Stranraer	Braemar
Dumbarton	Dunfermline
Cumbernauld	Kirkcaldy
Stirling	Stornoway

Teacher's notes

Sheet A, Look, listen and learn: Use the words on this page as a focus for discussing phonic patterns and word structures. What do the pupils notice about the set of words? Do they know that all of these towns are in Scotland or the Scottish islands? Most of the names have at least one graphical feature that does not follow conventional phonic rules. Can the pupils think of any towns in your area which have unusual spellings? Ask pairs or small groups of children to create two spoken sentences using some of the words

Sheet B, Look and write: Encourage the children to look closely at the words and to practise writing them.

Sheet B, Listen and write: Dictate each sentence below to the children, emphasising the target words and the revision words. Encourage the children to copy each sentence in full on the line underneath it. You could extend the activity by asking the children to make up their own sentence using one or more of the target words.

The capital city of Scotland is Edinburgh. Lerwick is the capital of the Shetland Islands.
You can catch a ferry from Stranraer to Belfast. The 'new town' of Cumbernauld was built in 1956.
Stornoway is on the Isle of Lewis in the Outer Hebrides.

Name Date

Look and write

Edinburgh	Lerwick
Stranraer	Braemar
Dumbarton	Dunfermline
Cumbernauld	Kirkcaldy
Stirling	Stornoway

Listen and write

The ________ city of Scotland is ________.

________ is the capital of the Shetland Islands.

You can catch a ferry from ________ to ________.

The 'new town' of ________ was built in 1956.

________ is on the Isle of Lewis in the Outer Hebrides.

Look, listen and learn

Cardiff	Aberystwyth
Swansea	Cwmbran
Merthyr Tydfil	Pontypridd
Llanelli	Carmarthen
Machynlleth	Ffestiniog

Teacher's notes

Sheet A, Look, listen and learn: Use the words on this page as a focus for discussing phonic patterns and word structures. What do the pupils notice about the set of words? Do they know that all of these towns are in Wales? Most of the names have at least one graphical feature that does not follow conventional phonic rules. Note that the grapheme 'f' represents the phoneme /v/, the grapheme 'ff' represents the phoneme /f/ and the grapheme /dd/ represents the phoneme /th/; the grapheme /ll/ cannot be pronounced correctly using any of the English phonemes! Can the pupils think of any towns in your area which have unusual spellings? Ask pairs or small groups of children to create two spoken sentences using some of the words.

Sheet B, Look and write: Encourage the children to look closely at the words and to practise writing them.

Sheet B, Listen and write: Dictate each sentence below to the children, emphasising the target words. Encourage the children to copy each sentence in full on the line underneath it. You could extend the activity by asking the children to make up their own sentence using one or more of the target words.

Cardiff is the tenth largest city in the United Kingdom of Great Britain and Northern Ireland.
There is a famous university in Aberystwyth. Merthyr Tydfil is not far from Pontypridd.
Carmarthen and Llanelli are both in Carmarthenshire. Ffestiniog is in the county of Gwynedd.

Name Date

Look and write

Cardiff	Aberystwyth
Swansea	Cwmbran
Merthyr Tydfil	Pontypridd
Llanelli	Carmarthen
Machynlleth	Ffestiniog

Listen and write

__________ is the tenth largest city in the United Kingdom of Great __________ and Northern __________.

There is a famous __________ in __________.

__________ is not far from __________.

__________ and __________ are both in __________.

__________ is in the county of __________.

Look, listen and learn

Belfast	Enniskillen
Omagh	Armagh
Carrickfergus	Magherafelt
Strabane	Limerick
Dublin	Tralee

Teacher's notes

Sheet A, Look, listen and learn: Use the words on this page as a focus for discussing phonic patterns and word structures. Wha[t] do the pupils notice about the set of words? Do they know that all of these towns are in Northern Ireland or the Republic of Ireland[?] Most of the names have at least one graphical feature that does not follow conventional phonic rules. Can the pupils think of any towns in your area which have unusual spellings? Ask pairs or small groups of children to create two spoken sentences using some [of] the words.

Sheet B, Look and write: Encourage the children to look closely at the words and to practise writing them.

Sheet B, Listen and write: Dictate each sentence below to the children, emphasising the target words. Show pupils the spelling o[f] Fermanagh before starting the dictation. Encourage the children to copy each sentence in full on the line underneath it. You could extend the activity by asking the children to make up their own sentence using one or more of the target words.

The capital of Northern Ireland is Belfast. Dublin is the capital of the Republic of Ireland.
The town of Enniskillen is in the county of Fermanagh. A type of rhyming poem is named after the city of Limerick.
Omagh and Strabane are both in County Tyrone.

Name Date

Look and write

Belfast	Enniskillen
Omagh	Armagh
Carrickfergus	Magherafelt
Strabane	Limerick
Dublin	Tralee

Listen and write

The capital of ______ Ireland is ______.

______ is the capital of the ______ of Ireland.

The town of ______ is in the county of ______.

A type of ______ poem is named after the city of ______.

______ and ______ are both in County Tyrone.

Look, listen and learn

Sydney	Beijing
Tokyo	Nairobi
Brasilia	Bratislava
Moscow	Montreal
Muscat	Mecca

Teacher's notes

Sheet A, Look, listen and learn: Use the words on this page as a focus for discussing phonic patterns and word structures. The list features the names of world cities, most of which are spelt following conventional phonic patterns and provide good practice of syllabification and segmentation. Note that the city of Brasilia is spelt with a letter 's'. Ask pairs or small groups of children to create two spoken sentences using some of the words.

Sheet B, Look and write: Encourage the children to look closely at the words and to practise writing them.

Sheet B, Listen and write: Dictate each sentence below to the children, emphasising the target words and the revision words. Show the pupils the spelling of the word 'Russia' before starting the dictation. Encourage the children to copy each sentence in full o the line underneath it. You could extend the activity by asking the children to make up their own sentence using one or more of the target words.

The city of Brasilia is the capital of Brazil. Sydney is a major city in Australia but it is not the capital.
Moscow is the capital city of Russia. Muscat and Mecca are both cities in the Middle East.
Montreal is the second largest city in Canada.

Name Date

Look and write

Sydney	Beijing
Tokyo	Nairobi
Brasilia	Bratislava
Moscow	Montreal
Muscat	Mecca

Listen and write

The city of ____________________ is the capital of ____________________.

____

____________________ is a major city in ________________________ but it is not the capital.

____

____________________ is the capital city of ____________________.

____

____________________ and ____________________ are both cities in the Middle East.

____

________________________ is the second largest city in ____________________.

____

SET 29 SHEET A

Look, listen and learn

calculator	doctor
instructor	reflector
inspector	junior
interior	exterior
escalator	commentator

Teacher's notes

Sheet A, Look, listen and learn: Use the words on this page as a focus for discussing phonic patterns and word structures. Can the children identify what the words have in common? Ask pairs or small groups of children to create two spoken sentences using some of the words.

Sheet B, Look and write: Encourage the children to look closely at the words and to practise writing them.

Sheet B, Listen and write: Dictate each sentence below to the children, emphasising the target words and the revision words. Show the pupils the spelling of the words 'customers', 'analysis' and 'senior' before starting the dictation. Encourage the children to copy each sentence in full on the line underneath it. You could extend the activity by asking the children to make up their own sentence using one or more of the target words.

The junior doctor works very long hours in the hospital. The escalator takes customers from one floor to another.
The exterior of the house was painted pink and the interior was all white.
After the football match, the commentator gave his analysis of the game. The instructor was coaching the senior pupils.

Name Date

Look and write

calculator

doctor

instructor

reflector

inspector

junior

interior

exterior

escalator

commentator

Listen and write

The ______ ______ works very long hours in the ______.

The ______ takes ______ from one floor to another.

The ______ of the house was painted pink and the ______ was all white.

After the football match, the ______ gave his ______ of the game.

The ______ was coaching the ______ pupils.

Look, listen and learn

estuary	temporary
primary	secondary
voluntary	tertiary
factory	laboratory
publicity	activity

Teacher's notes

Sheet A, Look, listen and learn: Use the words on this page as a focus for discussing phonic patterns and word structures. Encourage the children to observe the three different endings – can they think of other words that have the same endings? Ask pairs or small groups of children to create two spoken sentences using some of the words.

Sheet B, Look and write: Encourage the children to look closely at the words and to practise writing them.

Sheet B, Listen and write: Dictate each sentence below to the children, emphasising the target words. Encourage the children to copy each sentence in full on the line underneath it. You could extend the activity by asking the children to make up their own sentence using one or more of the target words.

Secondary education follows primary education and tertiary education follows secondary education.
Many people help others through voluntary work. A river enters the sea at an estuary.
The sports centre gained publicity for the summer activity week. There is a laboratory at the factory.

Name _______ Date _______

Look and write

estuary	temporary
primary	secondary
voluntary	tertiary
factory	laboratory
publicity	activity

Listen and write

__________ education follows __________ education and __________ education follows __________ education.

____

____

Many __________ help others through __________ work.

____

A river enters the sea at an __________.

____

The sports centre gained __________ for the summer __________ week.

____

There is a __________ at the __________.

____

SET 31 **SHEET A**

Look, listen and learn

adventure	adventurous
signature	agriculture
temperature	popular
popularity	particular
particularly	unpopular

Teacher's notes

Sheet A, Look, listen and learn: Use the words on this page as a focus for discussing phonic patterns and word structures. The list features words that end with 'ture' or 'ar' and others with extra suffixes added to these endings. Ask pairs or small groups of children to create two spoken sentences using some of the words.

Sheet B, Look and write: Encourage the children to look closely at the words and to practise writing them.

Sheet B, Listen and write: Dictate each sentence below to the children, emphasising the target words and the revision words. Encourage the children to copy each sentence in full on the line underneath it. You could extend the activity by asking the children to make up their own sentence using one or more of the target words.

I'm quite an adventurous person so I like adventure stories. The film star wrote her signature in my autograph book.
Agriculture is important in this country. The temperature is particularly cold today.
It's difficult to compare the popularity of different films.

Name Date

Look and write

adventure	adventurous
signature	agriculture
temperature	popular
popularity	particular
particularly	unpopular

Listen and write

I'm quite an ________ person so I like ________ stories.

The film star wrote her ________ in my ________ book.

________ is important in this ________.

The ________ is ________ cold today.

It's difficult to ________ the ________ of different films.

Look, listen and learn

different	difference
experience	independent
independently	independence
confident	confidently
confidential	influence

Teacher's notes

Sheet A, Look, listen and learn: Use the words on this page as a focus for discussing phonic patterns and word structures. This list features words that end with 'ent' or 'ence' and others with further suffixes added to these words. Ask pairs or small groups of children to create two spoken sentences using some of the words.

Sheet B, Look and write: Encourage the children to look closely at the words and to practise writing them.

Sheet B, Listen and write: Dictate each sentence below to the children, emphasising the target words and the revision words. Encourage the children to copy each sentence in full on the line underneath it. You could extend the activity by asking the children to make up their own sentence using one or more of the target words.

I enjoy having a variety of different experiences at the summer camp. The teacher says we should work independently.
He stepped confidently to the end of the diving board then dived into the pool perfectly.
The spy discovered some confidential information. Older pupils should have a good influence on younger pupils.

Name Date

Look and write

different	difference
experience	independent
independently	independence
confident	confidently
confidential	influence

Listen and write

I enjoy having a variety of ______ ______ at the summer camp.

______

The ______ says we should work ______.

______

He stepped ______ to the end of the diving ______ then dived into the pool ______.

______

______

The spy ______ some ______ information.

______

Older pupils should have a good ______ on ______ pupils.

______

Look, listen and learn

distant	distantly
distance	guide
guidance	important
importantly	importance
nuisance	balance

Teacher's notes

Sheet A, Look, listen and learn: Use the words on this page as a focus for discussing phonic patterns and word structures. The words can be compared to those on the previous list. Note that these words feature the endings 'ant' and 'ance', together with other where further suffixes have been added. Ask pairs or small groups of children to create two spoken sentences using some of the words

Sheet B, Look and write: Encourage the children to look closely at the words and to practise writing them.

Sheet B, Listen and write: Dictate each sentence below to the children, emphasising the target words and the revision words. Note the spelling of realized – this is the spelling given in the Oxford dictionary, though realised is shown as an acceptable alternative Encourage the children to copy each sentence in full on the line underneath it. You could extend the activity by asking the children to make up their own sentence using one or more of the target words.

The light from distant stars takes many years to reach the Earth.
I followed the guide for a great distance along the track before I realized that he was lost too!
As well as showing us spellings, a dictionary gives us important guidance on how to use words.
My little sister understood the importance of not being a nuisance in the cinema. Can you balance on the beam?

Name Date

Look and write

distant	distantly
distance	guide
guidance	important
importantly	importance
nuisance	balance

Listen and write

The light from ________ stars takes many years to ________ the Earth.

I ________ the ________ for a great ________ along the track before I realized that he was lost too!

As well as showing us spellings, a ________ gives us ________ on how to use words.

My little sister ________ the ________ of not being a ________ in the cinema.

Can you ________ on the beam?

Look, listen and learn

disguise	encyclopedia
government	parliament
rehearse	rehearsal
biscuit	catalogue
guarantee	equator

Teacher's notes

Sheet A, Look, listen and learn: Use the words on this page as a focus for discussing phonic patterns and word structures. This list consists of words that have a particularly unusual feature. Note that 'encyclopaedia' is an alternative spelling of 'encyclopedia'. You could suggest that the pupils add them to the class list of 'freaky' words started with the words in Set 23. Ask pairs or small groups of children to create two spoken sentences using some of the words.

Sheet B, Look and write: Encourage the children to look closely at the words and to practise writing them.

Sheet B, Listen and write: Dictate each sentence below to the children, emphasising the target words and the revision words. Note the spelling of 'recognize' – this is the spelling given in the Oxford dictionary, though 'recognise' is shown as an acceptable alternative. Encourage the children to copy each sentence in full on the line underneath it. You could extend the activity by asking th children to make up their own sentence using one or more of the target words.

The spy wore a disguise so that nobody would recognize her.
Now that we have the internet we don't often need to use an encyclopedia.
The Houses of Parliament are alongside the River Thames in London.
We had to rehearse every day for the school play. Our last rehearsal was in full costume.
I looked in a catalogue for a camera with a good guarantee.

Name Date

Look and write

disguise	encyclopedia
government	parliament
rehearse	rehearsal
biscuit	catalogue
guarantee	equator

Listen and write

The spy wore a ____________ so that nobody would ____________ her.

Now that we have the ____________ we don't often need to use an ____________.

The Houses of ____________ are alongside the River ____________ in London.

We had to ____________ every day for the school play. Our last ____________ was in full ____________.

I looked in a ____________ for a camera with a good ____________.

Look, listen and learn

neighbour	neighbourhood
neighbourly	behaviour
mischief	mischievous
encourage	encouragement
tourist	tourism

Teacher's notes

Sheet A, Look, listen and learn: Use the words on this page as a focus for discussing phonic patterns and word structures. Agai[n] this list consists of words that have a particularly unusual feature. Note that 'mischievous' is often mispronounced, with an extra /ee/ phoneme sounded after the letter 'v'. You could suggest that the pupils add the words to the class list of 'freaky' words started with the words in Set 23. Ask pairs or small groups of children to create two spoken sentences using some of the words.

Sheet B, Look and write: Encourage the children to look closely at the words and to practise writing them.

Sheet B, Listen and write: Dictate each sentence below to the children, emphasising the target words and the revision words. Encourage the children to copy each sentence in full on the line underneath it. You could extend the activity by asking the children t[o] make up their own sentence using one or more of the target words.

My next door neighbour says he doesn't like mischievous children. It's not very neighbourly to cause mischief in the street. Everybody in the neighbourhood went to the street party. The council likes to encourage tourists to visit the area. Tourism is very important to our country.

Name Date

Look and write

neighbour	neighbourhood
neighbourly	behaviour
mischief	mischievous
encourage	encouragement
tourist	tourism

Listen and write

My next door ______ says he ______ like ______ children.

______

______

It's not very ______ to cause ______ in the street.

______

______ in the ______ went to the street party.

______

The ______ likes to ______ ______ to visit the area.

______

______ is very important to our ______.

______

Look, listen and learn

converse	conversation
continent	continental
condition	conditional
consider	considerable
consideration	inconsiderable

Teacher's notes

Sheet A, Look, listen and learn: Use the words on this page as a focus for discussing phonic patterns and word structures. Do the pupils notice that all of the words feature the letter string 'con'? Can they think of other words that include this letter string? Ask pairs or small groups of children to create two spoken sentences using some of the words.

Sheet B, Look and write: Encourage the children to look closely at the words and to practise writing them.

Sheet B, Listen and write: Dictate each sentence below to the children, emphasising the target words and the revision words. Encourage the children to copy each sentence in full on the line underneath it. You could extend the activity by asking the children to make up their own sentence using one or more of the target words.

The converse of addition is subtraction. I had a long conversation about continents with my friend.
I've got a new bicycle because my old one was in very bad condition.
A considerable number of people went to the beach yesterday. We should all show consideration towards other people.

Name ______ Date ______

Look and write

converse	conversation
continent	continental
condition	conditional
consider	considerable
consideration	inconsiderable

Listen and write

The ______ of ______ is ______.

______

I had a long ______ about ______ with my friend.

______

I've got a new ______ ______ my old one was in very bad ______.

______

A ______ number of ______ went to the beach yesterday.

______

We should all show ______ towards other ______.

______

Look, listen and learn

continue	continuing
continued	continuation
continual	contain
container	contents
consume	consumption

Teacher's notes

Sheet A, Look, listen and learn: Use the words on this page as a focus for discussing phonic patterns and word structures. As with Set 36, these words all feature the letter string 'con'. Pupils should look closely at the extended words created from the base words 'continue' and 'consume'. Do they understand the relationship between the words 'contain' and 'contents'? Ask pairs or smal groups of children to create two spoken sentences using some of the words.

Sheet B, Look and write: Encourage the children to look closely at the words and to practise writing them.

Sheet B, Listen and write: Dictate each sentence below to the children, emphasising the target words and the revision words. Encourage the children to copy each sentence in full on the line underneath it. You could extend the activity by asking the children make up their own sentence using one or more of the target words.

If you don't complete your work, you will have to continue it later.
The television serial will be continued next week.
The game we played at lunchtime was a continuation of the one we started this morning.
Put your completed work in the correct container. I decided to consume the entire contents of the packet of biscuits.

Name Date

Look and write

continue	continuing
continued	continuation
continual	contain
container	contents
consume	consumption

Listen and write

If you don't ____________________ your work, you will have to ____________________ it later.

____

The ____________________ serial will be ____________________ next week.

____

The game we played at lunchtime was a ____________________ of the one we started this morning.

____

Put your ____________________ work in the ____________________ ____________________.

____

I decided to ____________________ the entire ____________________ of the packet of ____________________.

____

Look, listen and learn

aquarium	aquamarine
aquatic	aquanaut
aqueduct	hydrofoil
hydraulic	dehydrate
dehydration	hydrogen

Teacher's notes

Sheet A, Look, listen and learn: Use the words on this page as a focus for discussing phonic patterns and word structures. Explain to the pupils that the letter string 'aqua' is derived from the Latin for 'water' and the strings 'hydro' and 'hydra' are derived from the Greek. Ask pairs or small groups of children to create two spoken sentences using some of the words.

Sheet B, Look and write: Encourage the children to look closely at the words and to practise writing them.

Sheet B, Listen and write: Dictate each sentence below to the children, emphasising the target words. Encourage the children to copy each sentence in full on the line underneath it. You could extend the activity by asking the children to make up their own sentence using one or more of the target words.

I have thirty-four fish in my aquarium. A story concerned some aquanauts who were exploring some underwater caves.
The boats collided when they were crossing the aqueduct.
The hull of a hydrofoil rises out of the water so that the vessel can go faster. Water is a compound of oxygen and hydrogen.

SET 38 SHEET B

Name Date

Look and write

aquarium	aquamarine
aquatic	aquanaut
aqueduct	hydrofoil
hydraulic	dehydrate
dehydration	hydrogen

Listen and write

I have thirty-four fish in my ______________________.

____

A story ______________________ some ______________________ who were ______________________ some underwater caves.

____

The boats ______________________ when they were crossing the ______________________.

____

The hull of a ______________________ rises out of the water so that the ______________________ can go faster.

____

____

Water is a ______________________ of oxygen and ______________________.

____

Look, listen and learn

audition	audible
audience	auditorium
audibly	visual
visible	visibility
invisible	audio-visual

Teacher's notes

Sheet A, Look, listen and learn: Use the words on this page as a focus for discussing phonic patterns and word structures. Explain to the pupils that the letter string 'audi' is derived from the Latin for 'hear' and that 'vis' is derived from the Latin for 'see'. As pairs or small groups of children to create two spoken sentences using some of the words.

Sheet B, Look and write: Encourage the children to look closely at the words and to practise writing them.

Sheet B, Listen and write: Dictate each sentence below to the children, emphasising the target words and the revision words. Encourage the children to copy each sentence in full on the line underneath it. You could extend the activity by asking the children to make up their own sentence using one or more of the target words.

The girl went for an audition to take part in a performance of an opera.
The sound of an aeroplane is audible above the noise from the vehicles on the main road.
The audience were packed tightly into the auditorium. When it's misty, the visibility on the motorway is greatly reduced.
A huge range of audio-visual equipment is now available.

Name Date

Look and write

audition	audible
audience	auditorium
audibly	visual
visible	visibility
invisible	audio-visual

Listen and write

The girl went for an ______ to take part in a ______ of an opera.

The sound of an aeroplane is ______ above the noise from the ______ on the main road.

The ______ were packed tightly into the ______.

When it's misty, the ______ on the motorway is greatly ______.

A huge range of ______ equipment is now ______.

Look, listen and learn

subject	submarine
submariner	subtitle
subtotal	subsoil
substandard	subsequent
subsequently	subtle

Teacher's notes

Sheet A, Look, listen and learn: Use the words on this page as a focus for discussing phonic patterns and word structures. All o the words feature the prefix 'sub' – can the pupils think of other words with this prefix? Ask pairs or small groups of children to crea two spoken sentences using some of the words.

Sheet B, Look and write: Encourage the children to look closely at the words and to practise writing them.

Sheet B, Listen and write: Dictate each sentence below to the children, emphasising the target words and the revision words. Discuss the word 'enthusiastically', encouraging the pupils to attempt to spell it by using their skills in syllabification and segmentation. Encourage the children to copy each sentence in full on the line underneath it. You could extend the activity by askin the children to make up their own sentence using one or more of the target words.

"What subjects are we working on this afternoon, Miss?" asked the boy enthusiastically.
More than eighty submariners make up the crew of a nuclear submarine.
Mum complained that the workmanship on the cupboard was substandard.
The topsoil was easy to dig through but the subsoil was full of stones. The subtitle of the book was longer than the main title.

Name Date

Look and write

subject	submarine
submariner	subtitle
subtotal	subsoil
substandard	subsequent
subsequently	subtle

Listen and write

"What ________ are we working on this afternoon, Miss?" asked the boy ________.

More than eighty ________ make up the crew of a nuclear ________.

Mum complained that the ________ on the ________ was ________.

The ________ was easy to dig through but the ________ was full of stones.

The ________ of the book was longer than the main ________.

Look, listen and learn

superb	superbly
superficial	superficially
superfluous	superintendent
superhero	supernova
superior	supersonic

Teacher's notes

Sheet A, Look, listen and learn: Use the words on this page as a focus for discussing phonic patterns and word structures. The prefix 'super' is derived from the Latin for 'above' or 'beyond'. Ask pairs or small groups of children to create two spoken sentences using some of the words.

Sheet B, Look and write: Encourage the children to look closely at the words and to practise writing them.

Sheet B, Listen and write: Dictate each sentence below to the children, emphasising the target words and the revision words. Pay particular attention to the word 'sergeant' – this 'breaks' phonic rules in two places. Note also the plural of 'superhero' – do the children add the appropriate 'es' ending? Encourage the children to copy each sentence in full on the line underneath it. You could extend the activity by asking the children to make up their own sentence using one or more of the target words.

My mum said my performance in the play was superb! I only have a superficial knowledge of astronomy.
The police superintendent was accompanied by a constable, a sergeant and an inspector.
Batman and Superman are superior superheroes. A supernova is a star that suddenly becomes much brighter.

Name Date

Look and write

superb	superbly
superficial	superficially
superfluous	superintendent
superhero	supernova
superior	supersonic

Listen and write

My mum said my ______________ in the play was ______________!

I only have a ______________ ______________ of ______________.

The police ______________ was accompanied by a constable, a ______________ and an inspector.

Batman and Superman are ______________ ______________.

A ______________ is a star that ______________ becomes much ______________.

SET 42 SHEET A

Look, listen and learn

microphone	microscope
microscopic	microchip
microclimate	microlight
microwave	miniature
minimal	minimum

Teacher's notes

Sheet A, Look, listen and learn: Use the words on this page as a focus for discussing phonic patterns and word structures. The prefix 'micro' is derived from Greek and 'mini' is derived from Latin. Ask pairs or small groups of children to create two spoken sentences using some of the words.

Sheet B, Look and write: Encourage the children to look closely at the words and to practise writing them.

Sheet B, Listen and write: Dictate each sentence below to the children, emphasising the target words. Encourage the children to copy each sentence in full on the line underneath it. You could extend the activity by asking the children to make up their own sentence using one or more of the target words.

She looked shocked when she first used the microphone and heard her voice through the loudspeakers.
We looked at the microscopic insect through a microscope.
Our town seems to have its own microclimate as it's always raining here when it's dry everywhere else!
We heated the soup in the microwave for too long. We need a minimum of five people to take part in this concert.

Name Date

Look and write

microphone	microscope
microscopic	microchip
microclimate	microlight
microwave	miniature
minimal	minimum

Listen and write

She looked shocked when she first used the ______________ and heard her voice through the ______________.

____

____

We looked at the ______________ insect through a ______________.

____

Our town seems to have its own ______________ as it's always raining here when it's dry ______________ else!

____

____

We heated the soup in the ______________ for too long.

____

We need a ______________ of five people to take part in this ______________.

____

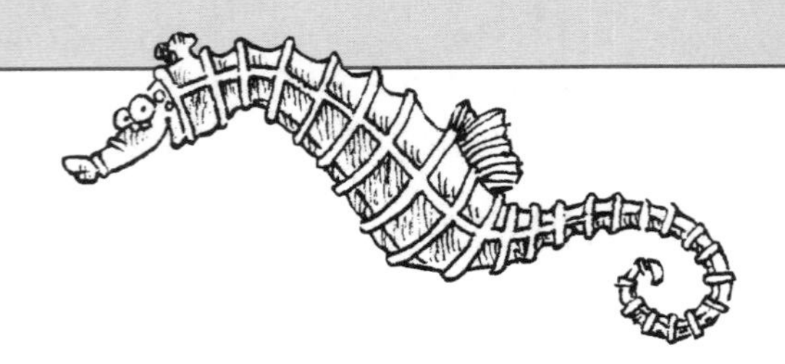

Assessment 1

My **favourite subject** is **mathematics**. I'm **interested** in **fractions**, **decimals** and **percentages** but **integers**, which are whole numbers, are more **fascinating**. I like playing with numbers, **investigating square** numbers, **factors** and **prime** numbers.

Work with shape is also very **interesting**. I enjoy making **accurate measurements** to find the **perimeters** of squares, rectangles, **hexagons**, **octagons** and other two **dimensional** shapes. **Circles** are more difficult to **measure**: the **radius** and the **diameter** are easy but the **circumference** is much harder.

Write about one of your school subjects.

Assessment 2

Last week I travelled from **Worcester** to **Scotland**. I had to call in to a shop in **Birmingham** on the way, then later I had to make a stop in **Middlesborough** and a further stop in **Berwick-upon-Tweed**, but **eventually** I crossed the **border**. A **couple** of hours later I reached **Edinburgh**. I was so pleased to see the **castle** again.

My **journey continued** the following day. I travelled north through **Braemar** and **Inverness** then **caught** the ferry from **Thurso** to Stromness in the **Orkney** Islands. I stayed there for one night then caught another ferry to go on to my final **destination**, **Lerwick** in the **Shetland** Islands.

Write about a journey you have made.

Assessment 3

The **aquanauts** approached the hull of the **submarine cautiously**. Ever since the **adventure** first began, this was the moment they had been **waiting** for. This was the perfect day for their **attack**. The **temperature** had **dropped**, so the **guards** on the **quayside** had become careless and hadn't **noticed** the **aquanauts** entering the water. The swim across the **harbour** had been easy and now they were ready.

Silently, the two **adventurers** used the **magnetism** of their **metallic** gloves to cling to the **submarine**. They began moving slowly, ensuring they made the **minimum** noise as they moved towards the **surface**.

What could happen next in this story?

Teacher's notes

The three assessment texts on the following page can be used to sample pupils' progress, giving a 'snapshot' of their current level o competence in spelling. Most of the words appear in the sets of words that the pupils have been practising but others are introduce as they follow similar patterns to known words or follow phonic rules. Do the pupils use skills in syllabification and segmentation effectively?

Assessment 1 features 25 mathematical vocabulary words to spell. Multiplying each pupil's score by 4 will give a percentage result. Assessments 2 and 3 both have 20 words to spell and therefore multiplying by 5 will give their percentages.

To administer each test, dictate the full passage before issuing the test sheets. Dictate the passage again very slowly, ensuring that each child is keeping up with your reading. Allow time for the children to write each of the missing words.

You may like to use the assessments on several occasions to identify any progress, using only one test on each occasion. Are there particular words or spelling patterns that cause difficulties for some children? If so, would the pupils benefit from revisiting the lists that feature these?

As an extra activity you could ask the pupils to extend each passage or to write their own passage of a similar type.

Assessment 1

Name Date

My ________________ ________________ is ________________. I'm ________________ in ________________, ________________ and ________________ but ________________, which are whole numbers, are more ________________. I like playing with numbers, ________________ ________________ numbers, ________________ and ________________ numbers.

Work with shape is also very ________________. I enjoy making ________________ ________________ to find the ________________ of squares, rectangles, ________________, ________________ and other two ________________ shapes. ________________ are more difficult to ________________: the ________________ and the ________________ are easy but the ________________ is much harder.

Score /25 = %

Assessment 2

Name Date

Last week I travelled from ________________ to ________________. I had to call in to a shop in ________________ on the way, then later I had to make a stop in ________________ and a further stop in ________________, but ________________ I crossed the ________________. A ________________ of hours later I reached ________________. I was so pleased to see the ________________ again.

My ________________ ________________ the following day. I travelled north through ________________ and ________________ then ________________ the ferry from ________________ to Stromness in the ________________ Islands. I stayed there for one night then caught another ferry to go on to my final ________________, ________________ in the ________________ Islands.

Score /20 = %

Assessment 3

Name Date

The ______________ approached the hull of the ______________
______________. Ever since the ______________ first began, this was the moment they had been ______________ for. This was the perfect day for their ______________. The ______________ had ______________, so the ______________ on the ______________ had become careless and hadn't ______________ the ______________ entering the water. The swim across the ______________ had been easy and now they were ready.

______________, the two ______________ used the ______________ of their ______________ gloves to cling to the ______________. They began moving slowly, ensuring they made the ______________ noise as they moved towards the ______________.

Score /20 = %